Piano Dreams

Solo pieces for piano

Book 2

by Anne Terzibaschitsch

Published by
Trinity College London Press
www.trinitycollege.com

Registered in England
Company no. 09726123

First impression, March 2016

Printed in England by Caligraving Ltd.
Music origination by Camden Music Services.
Illustrations by Ruth Keating.

Preface

Following the success of book 1 of *Piano Dreams*, I am pleased to present a further selection of pieces which I use in my own teaching.

The focus of this second volume is on the needs of more advanced pupils. The notes opposite provide some suggestions for playing each of the pieces.

Wishing all pianists, big and small, good luck and much joy in making music.

Anne Terzibaschitsch
Karlsruhe 1996

Contents

Notes

Moonlit Night (p6) is a 'song without words', a character piece in the Romantic style. The titles of character pieces are usually lyrical or poetic rather than 'musical', and reflect the mood, atmosphere, feelings or emotions evoked by the music.

In **Bird Flight** (p7), the left hand 'flies over' the right hand with a big swooping arm movement. The right hand moves only slightly from the wrist during the pauses. There is enough time to adjust the finger position in the right hand at the beginning of each bar.

The notes in small print immediately before the main notes in **The Goblin** (p8) are ornaments. These dissonant little notes are called grace notes (or acciaccaturas). They are played just before the beat which falls on the main note (almost at the same time) and are marked with an accent.

The melody of **Dream Horses** (p9) is characterised by repeated notes in the right hand. However, this should not impede the even flow of the triplets in the left hand.

The Little Ghost (p10) surprises us with its capricious (**Capriccioso**) and wayward notions. A *crescendo* is followed by a *subito* (sudden) *piano* and the piece is full of unexpected accents.

Witches' Dance (p11) is a study in chromatic scales which move up and down in semitones. The word chromatic comes from the Greek 'chroma' meaning colour.

In **Sleeping Beauty** (p12), maintain good flexibility in the wrist of the left hand so that the third finger can smoothly cross over the thumb. The right hand melody needs to sing out above the accompaniment.

In **The Good Fairy** (p14), left hand flexibility will allow the hand to span the wider spaced intervals. Be careful when reading the notes on the upper ledger lines. Add fingering 5-2-1 in music.

Playing the call of **The Cuckoo** (p15) requires confidence in changing position on the keyboard. In order to move the right hand to the upper position, pupils have to engage the upper arm.

The Mosquito (p16), a funny character piece, is a little study in trills for the right hand.

In **Hunting Scenes** (p18), there are three leitmotifs or themes (a leitmotif is a brief musical phrase that recurs throughout the piece and represents a person, scene or event). The hunters' theme starts with an ascending fourth (***mf***). An ascending fifth (***f***) represents the hunting horns while you can hear the hare in the second intervals (***p***).

From bar 10 onwards, the left hand in **Rush Hour** (p20) plays a discordant cluster of notes which consist of two pairs of semitones, just like the cars stuck in the rush hour traffic!

Mr Sandman (p21) introduces playing various descending and ascending intervals with the right hand. You need to be careful to keep your wrist supple.

The Old Man (p22) has a bleak, sad (**Mesto**) feel to it. It isn't easy to play the melody in the right hand and it requires pedalling before the first and second beats in each bar.

In the piano piece **Autumn Leaf in the Wind** (p23), the descending and ascending right hand motifs reflect the fluttering of the leaf in the wind. The repeated theme reinforces the melancholy (**Malinconico**) mood.

The fluttering wings of **The Butterfly** (p24) are represented by the *leggiero* (Italian for 'light') semiquaver figure in the right hand, so keep the right hand touch as delicate as possible.

The melody in **The Baby Elephant's Waltz** (p26) is in the bass line. The chords in the right hand are there for accompaniment.

In **Song of the Angels** (p28) the left hand swoops over the right hand. It is important to remember that the general dynamic level remains at ***mp*** until the final bars. The word *amabile* implies a tender and gentle approach.

In **The Old Gramophone** (p30) the opening figure which turns about on itself, requires a gentle placing of the thumb as it prepares to move into the following bar. Look out for the bar marked *ad lib.*, which represents where the needle gets stuck on the record. Play this bar as many times as you like – have fun!

The Little Locomotive (p33) sets off slowly. Bit by bit, it speeds up (*accelerando*). Little by little it reaches full speed (*allegro*). It whistles loudly (major second) as it steams happily along. As its destination comes into sight, it slows to a halt (**rit.**, *dim.*). With a final blast of the whistle, it stops.

The Little Elf (p34) dances gracefully (*grazioso*) in the first section and sings (*cantabile*) beautifully in the middle section. The dance-like character of the piece is highlighted by the light emphasis on each beat at the start and end while the melody is 'sung' in *legato* phrases in the middle.

Ting-a-ling-a-ling (p36), Christmas is here, is a song in three parts with the first section repeated at the end of the song (ABA form). The 'A' section is in E major and features high notes reflecting Santa's sleigh flying high in the sky, while the melody in the 'B' section is played lower down the keyboard in C major and represents the family opening presents below.

The Walk (p37) starts off with a happy mood as the walker saunters along in a carefree manner. Listen for the change to the minor key. What do you think is happening to the walker?

The Alarm Clock (p39) is a piece of programme music. It describes a sequence of events in music. The term 'programme music' is more commonly used to describe instrumental music, for example, the symphonic poem *Ma Vlast* ('My homeland' in Czech) by Bedřich Smetana.

Look out for the programme behind **A Happy Find** (p40). The contrasting sections will help you share the boy's journey towards the lucky find.

The House Elf's Rag (p42) is a Ragtime piece (ragged time). This style of music developed in North America in the second half of the 19th century before becoming popular in Europe. Ragtime features the following rhythmic characteristics:

1. continuous strong bass notes on the first and third beat of each bar (left hand), and
2. syncopation on the offbeat in the melody (right hand).

Moonlit Night

26
rit.
3
pp

Bird Flight

Volante
3
l.h.
2
l.h.
2
2 4 sim.
2
p
5
5
Ped.
sim.
5
3
1
3
3
5
9
2
3
13
2
4
rit.
1 2 5 1 3 5
5
2
4
pp

The Goblin

Dream Horses

The Little Ghost

Witches' Dance

Sleeping Beauty

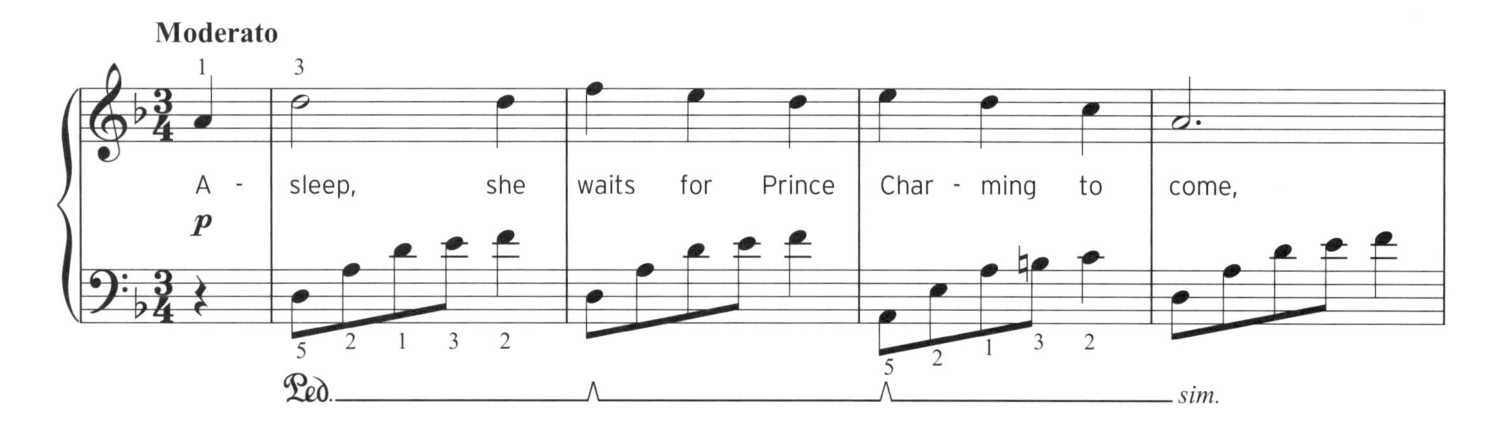

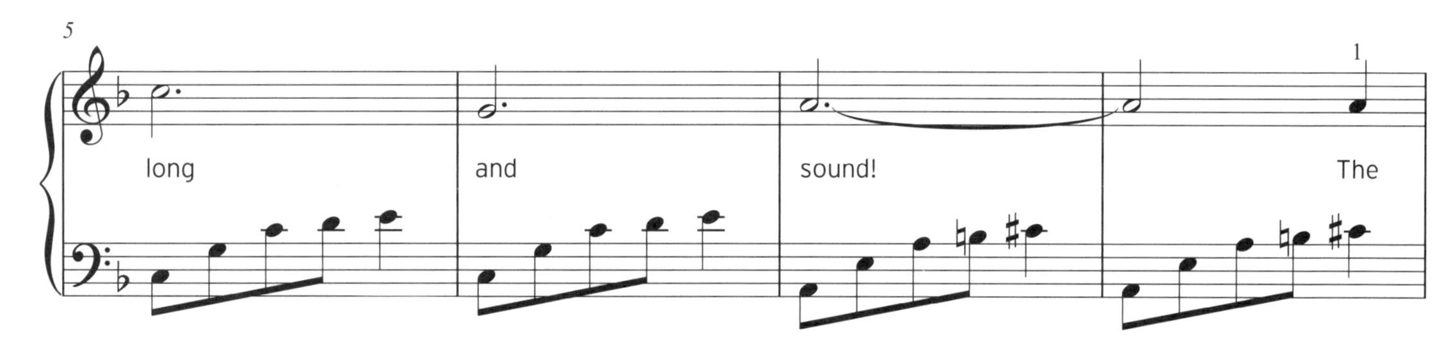

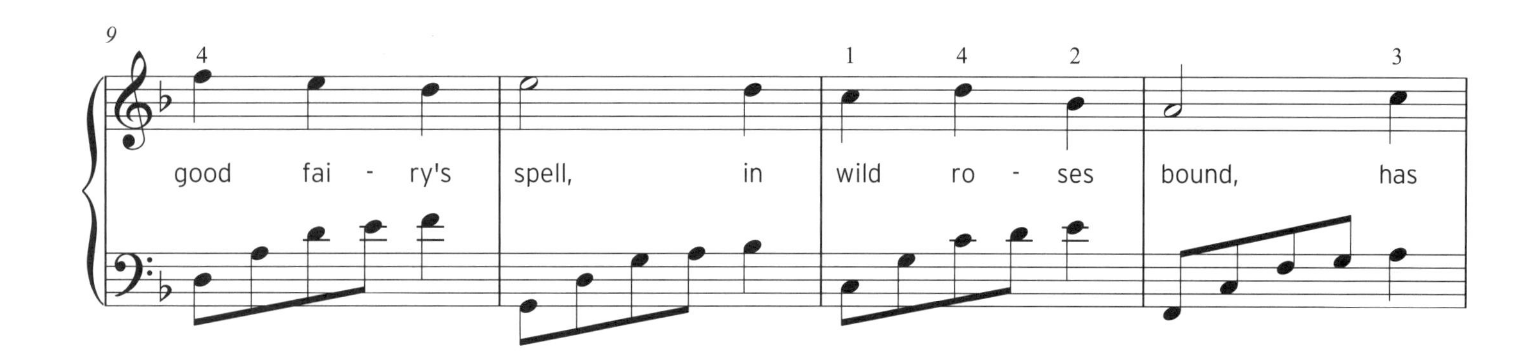

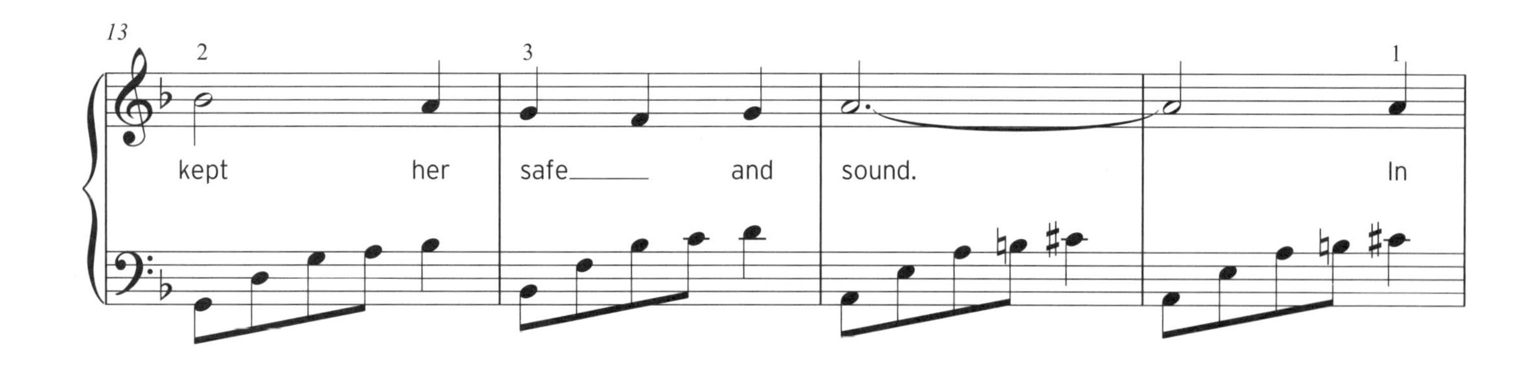

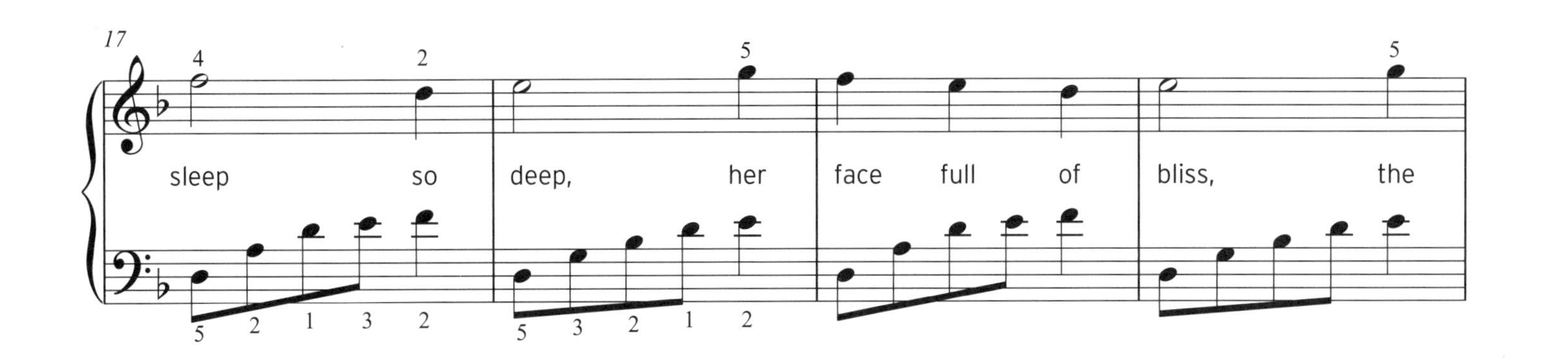
17
sleep so deep, her face full of bliss, the

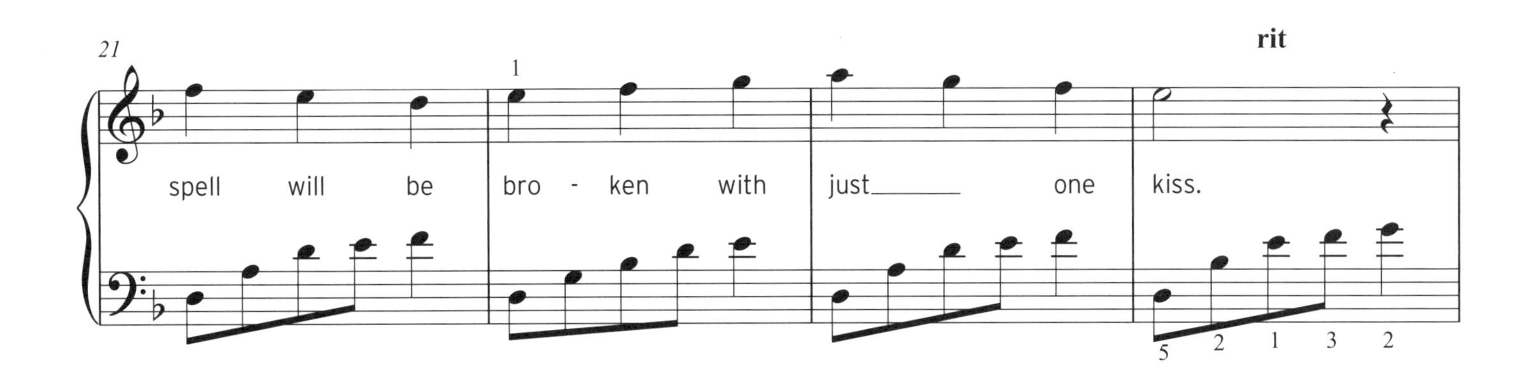
21
rit
spell will be bro - ken with just one kiss.

a tempo
25
Sweet dreams, sweet dreams, the

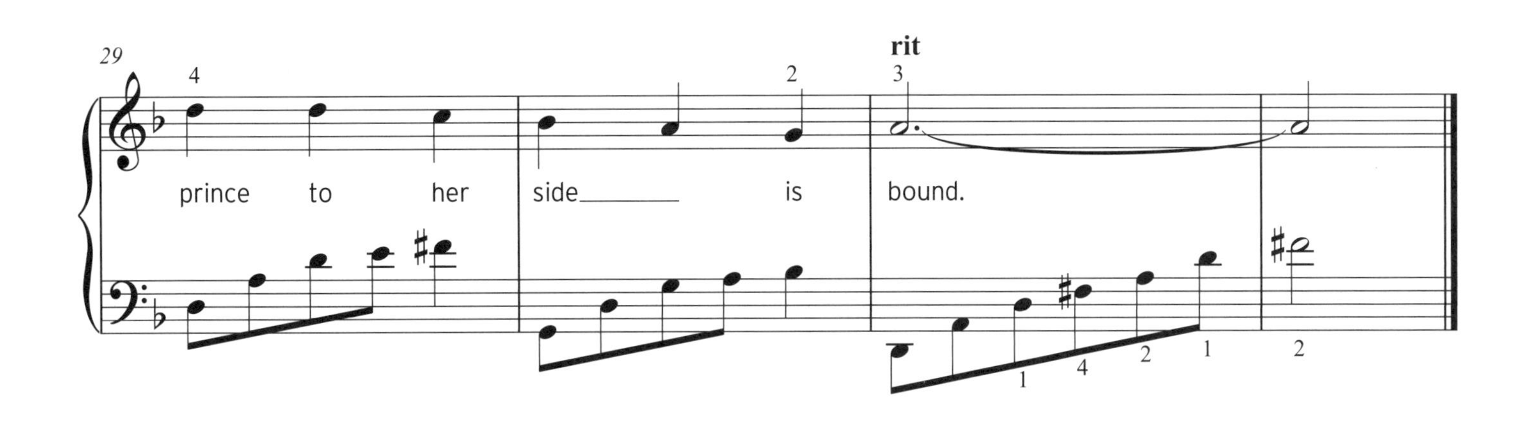
29
rit
prince to her side is bound.

The Good Fairy

The Cuckoo

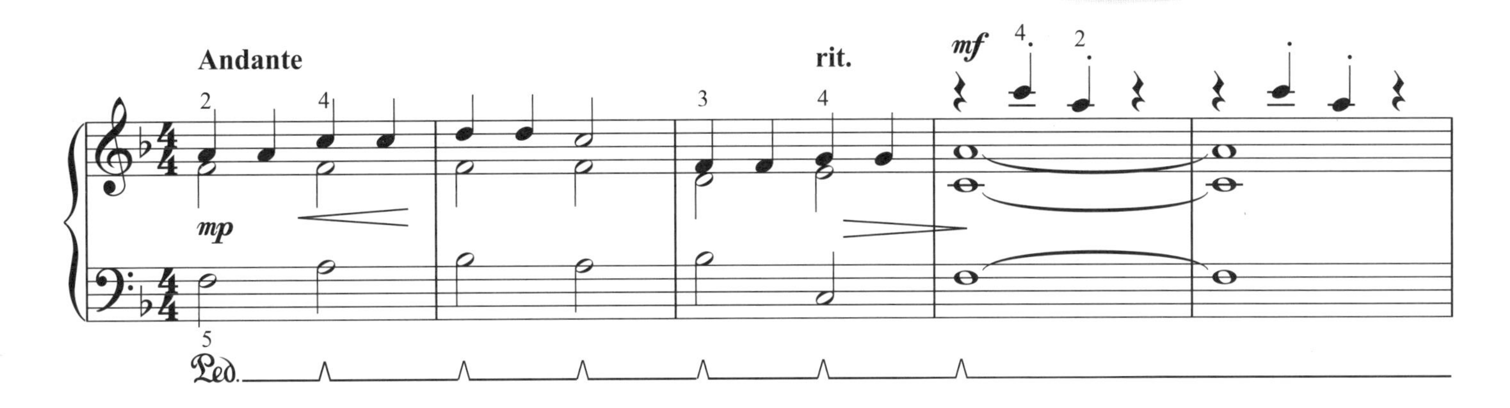
Andante
rit.
mf
mp
a tempo
rit.
mf
mp
sim.

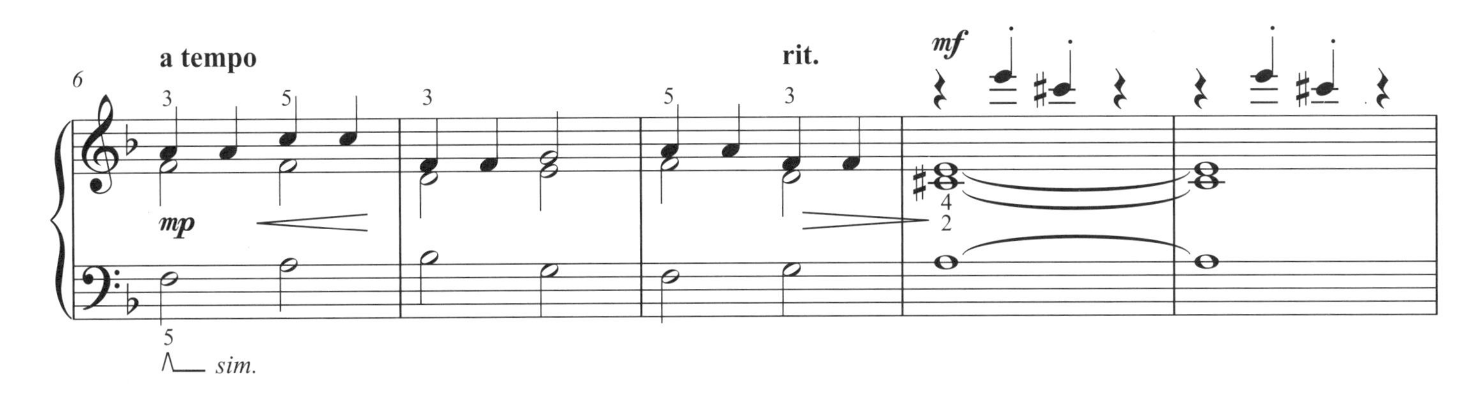

a tempo
rit.
mf
mp

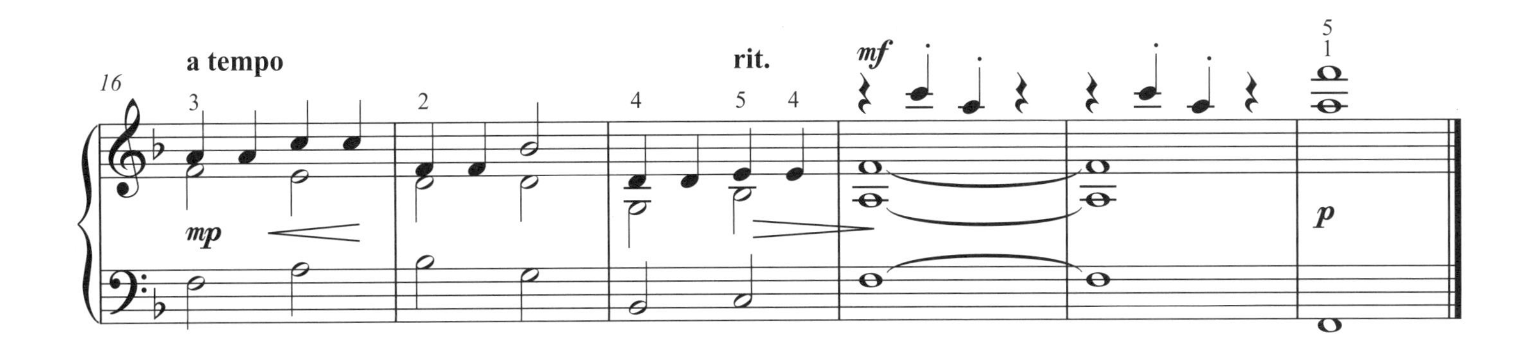
a tempo
rit.
mf
mp
p

The Mosquito

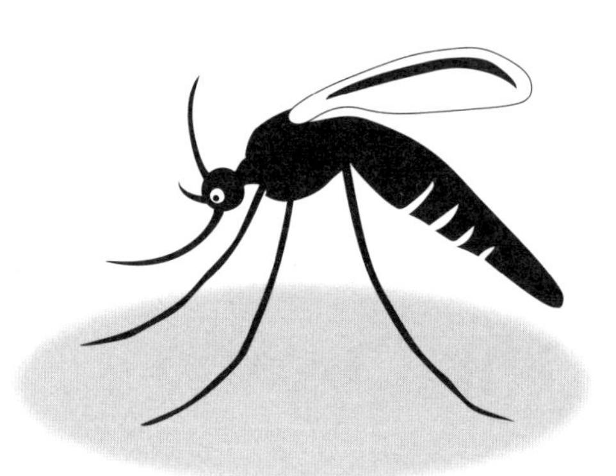

19
21
23
mf
26
30
p

Hunting Scenes

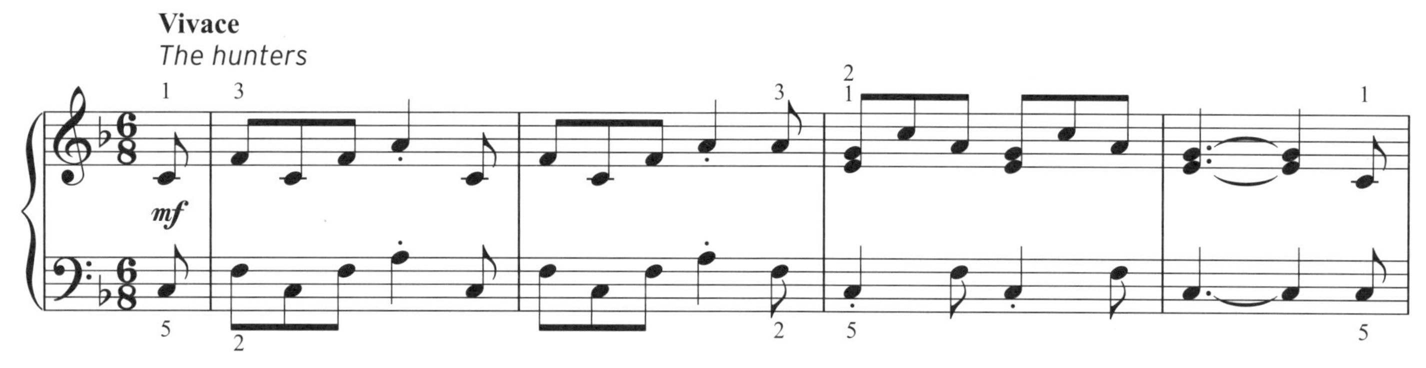

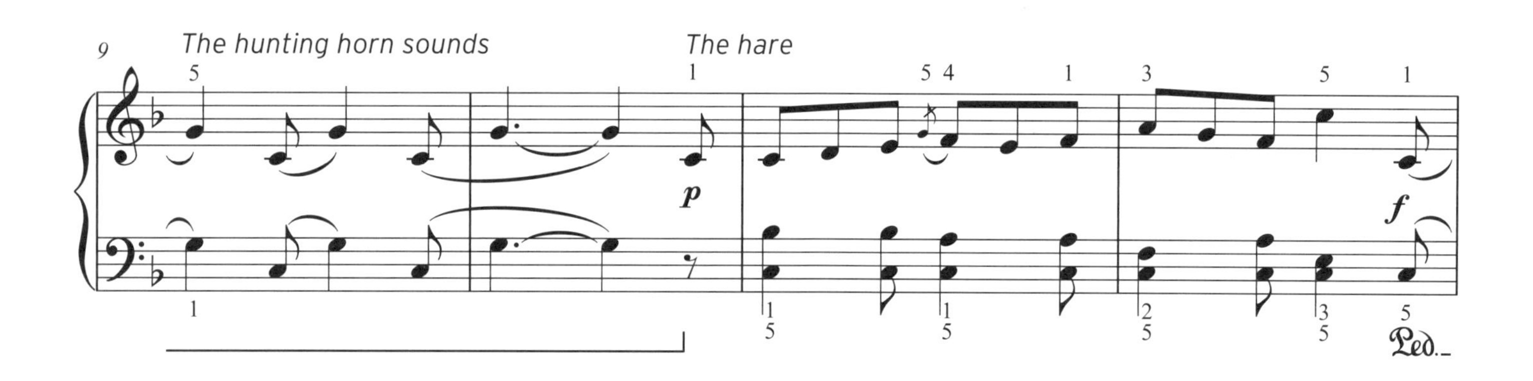

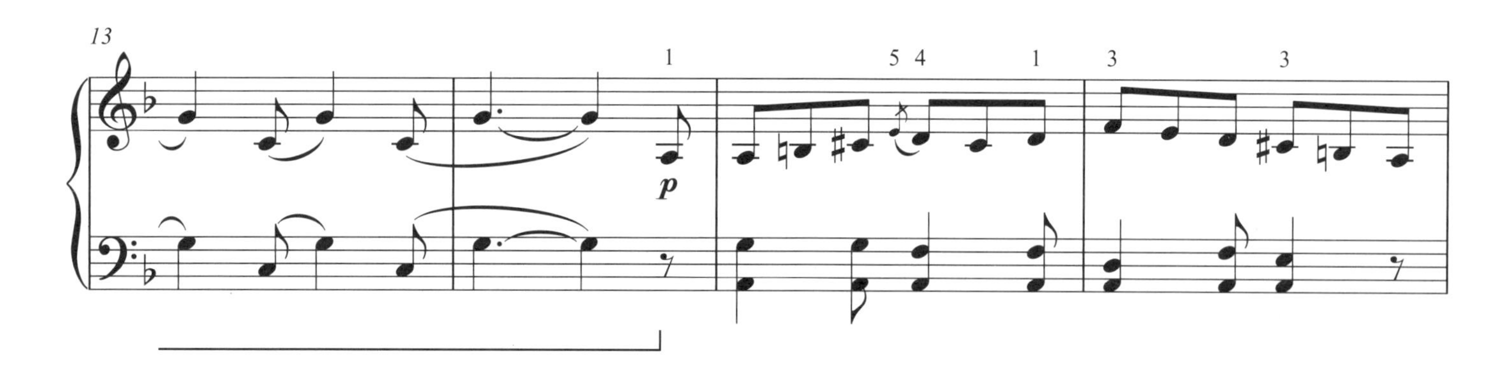

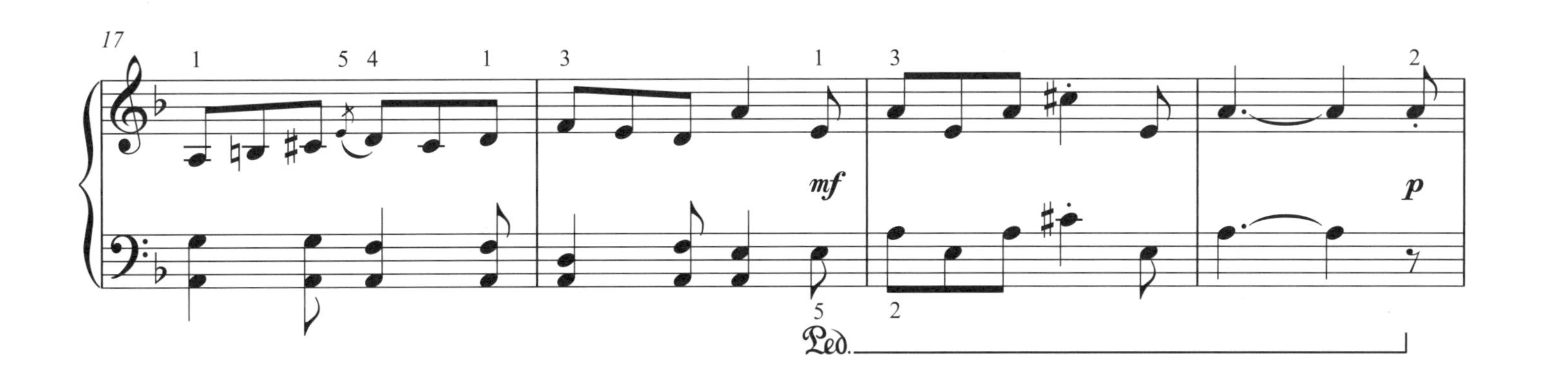
17
mf
p
Ped.

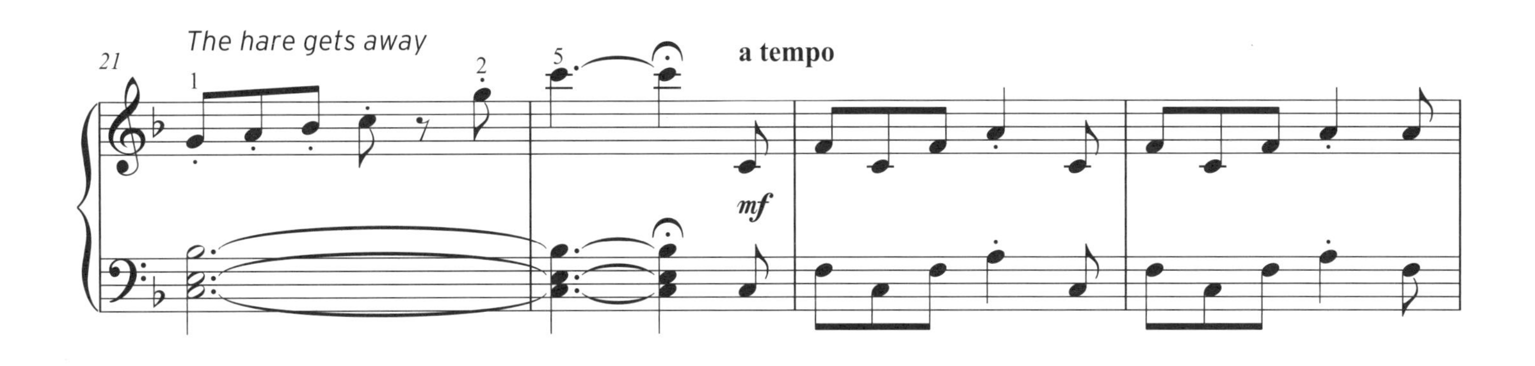
21
The hare gets away
a tempo
mf

25

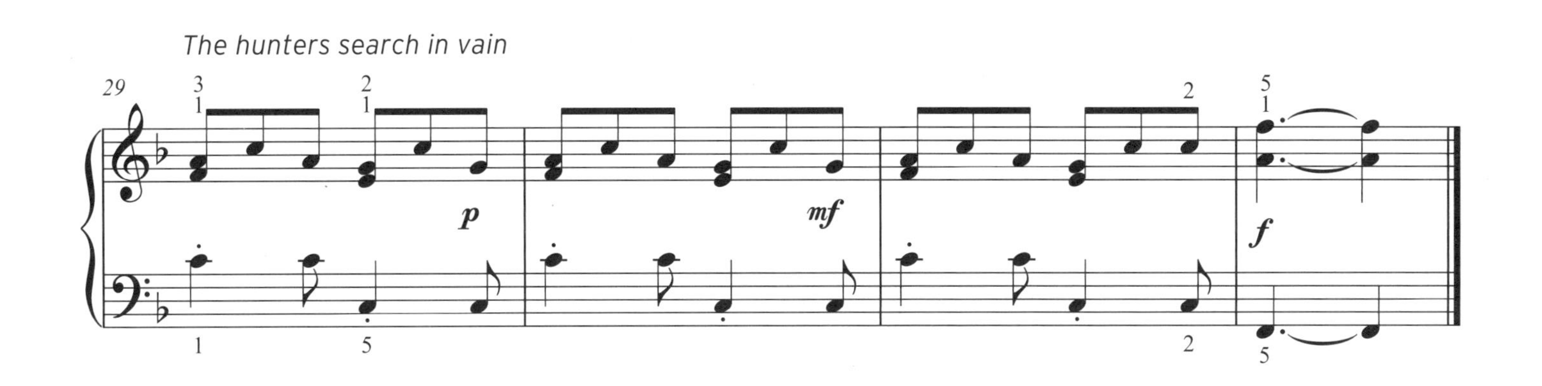
29
The hunters search in vain
p
mf
f

Rush Hour

Vivo
f
Red traffic lights
A child crosses the street singing
mf
mp
rit.
Green traffic lights
f

Mr Sandman

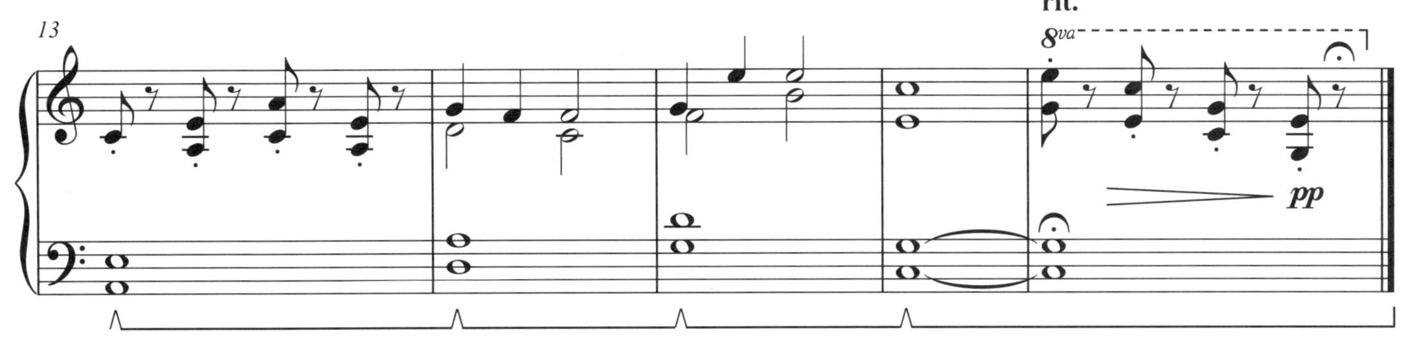

The Old Man

Autumn Leaf in the Wind

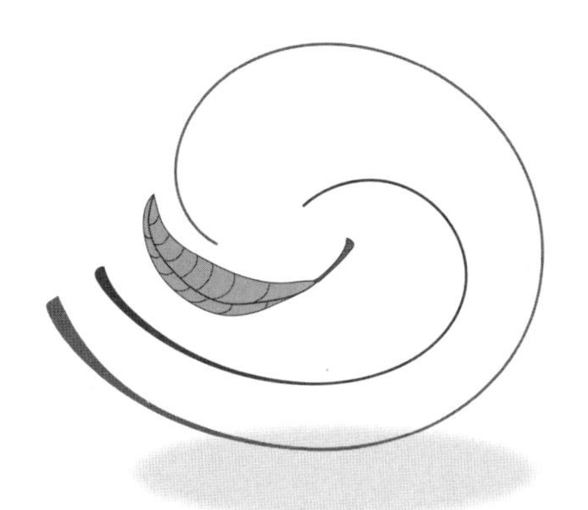

The Butterfly

11
14
17
19
dim.
21
rit.
pp

The Baby Elephant's Waltz

rit.
cresc.
a tempo

Song of the Angels

rit.
p

The Old Gramophone

rit.
a tempo
mf
sf
ad lib.
sf

Finale
Presto
sf
p
cresc.
ad lib.
rit.
sf
sf
f
ff

The Little Locomotive

The Little Elf

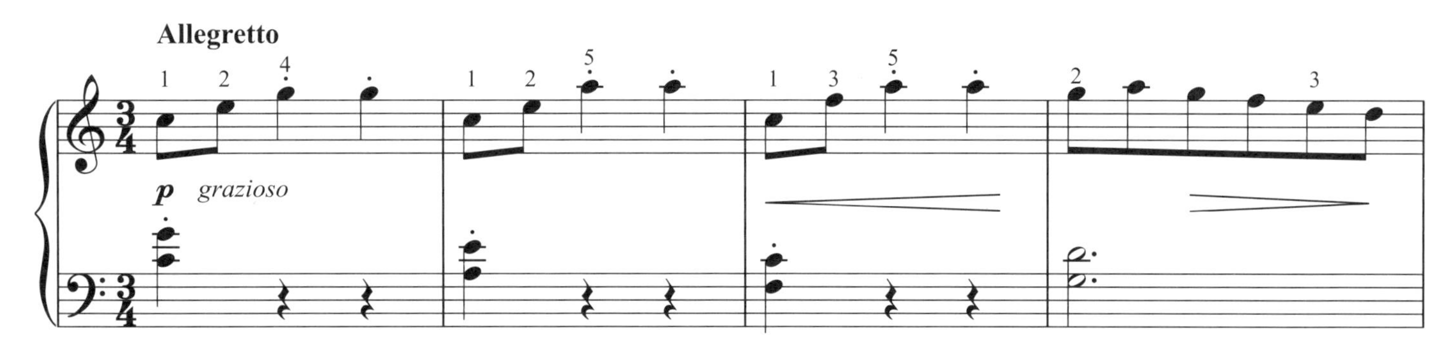

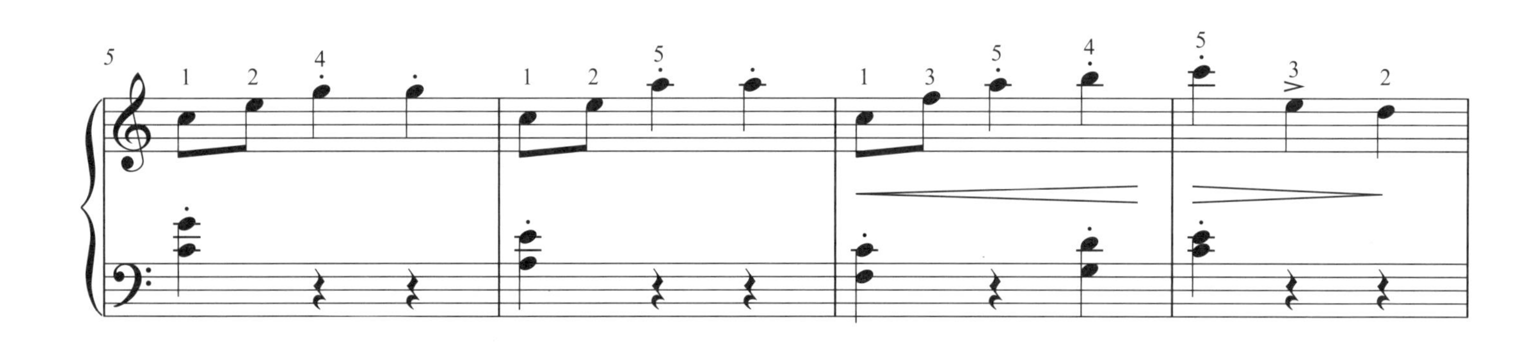

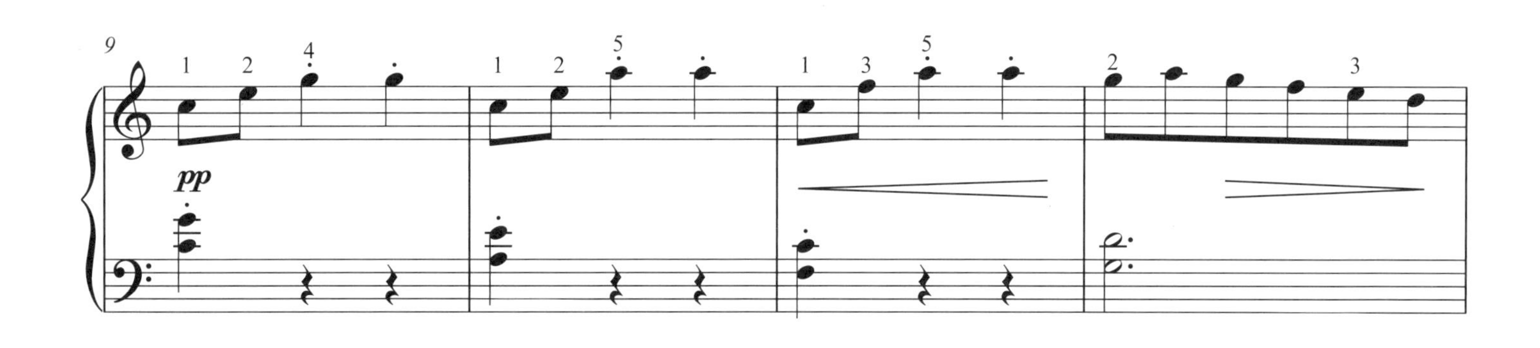

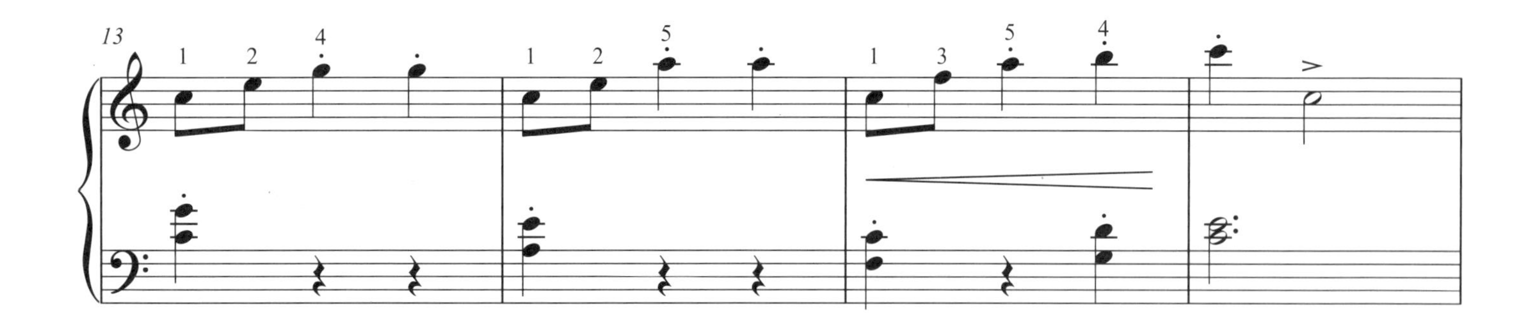

17
f cantabile
Ped.
21
p
25
pp
rit.
a tempo
p
29
33
rit.
pp

Ting-a-ling-a-ling

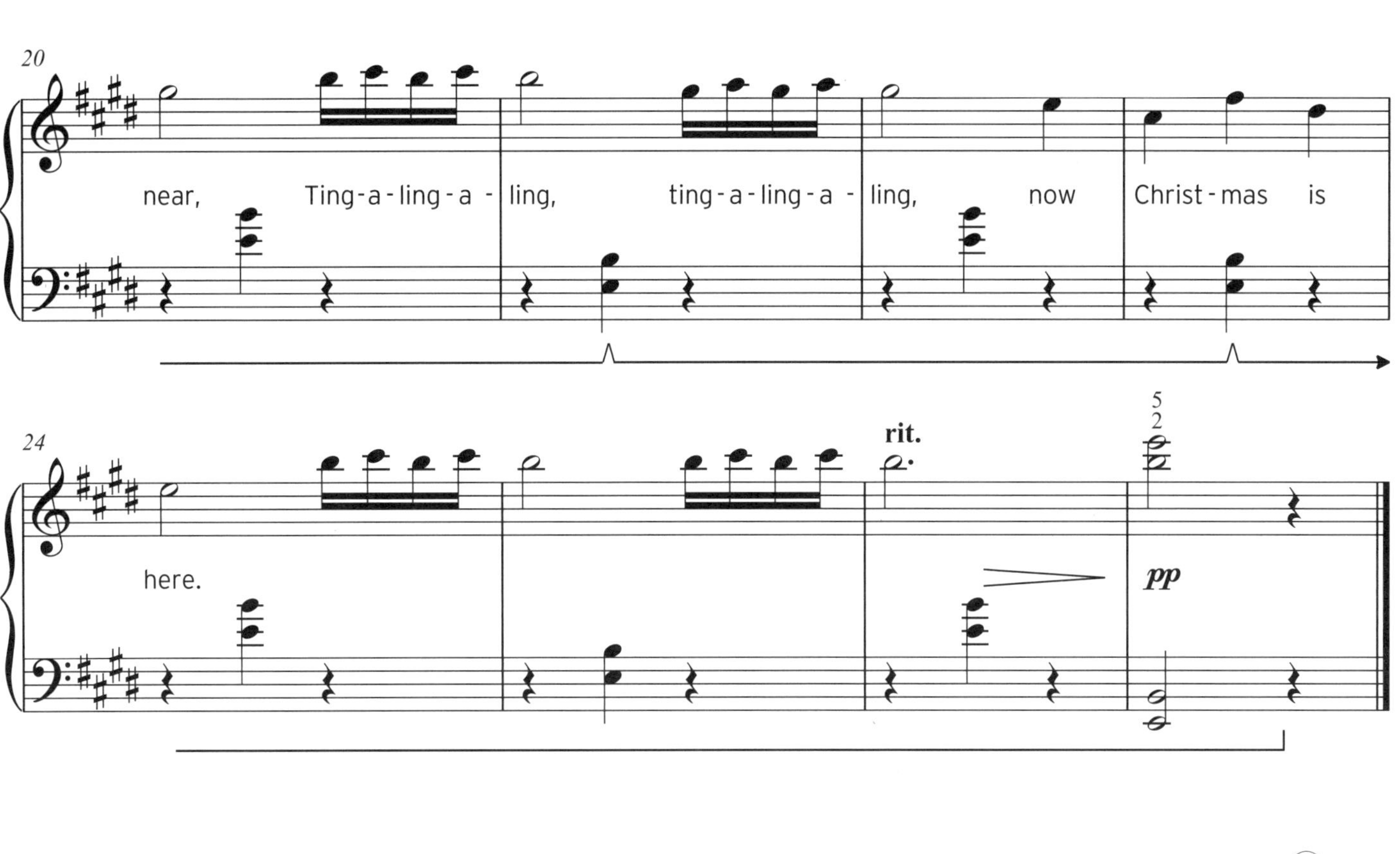
20
near, Ting-a-ling-a - ling, ting-a-ling-a - ling, now Christ-mas is
24
rit.
here.
pp

The Walk

Andante
f
p
mp
4

rit.
mf
cresc.
f
meno mosso
mp
Vivo
f
sf

The Alarm Clock

A Happy Find

Moderato
A boy walks alone through the streets
He comes across a fun fair

26

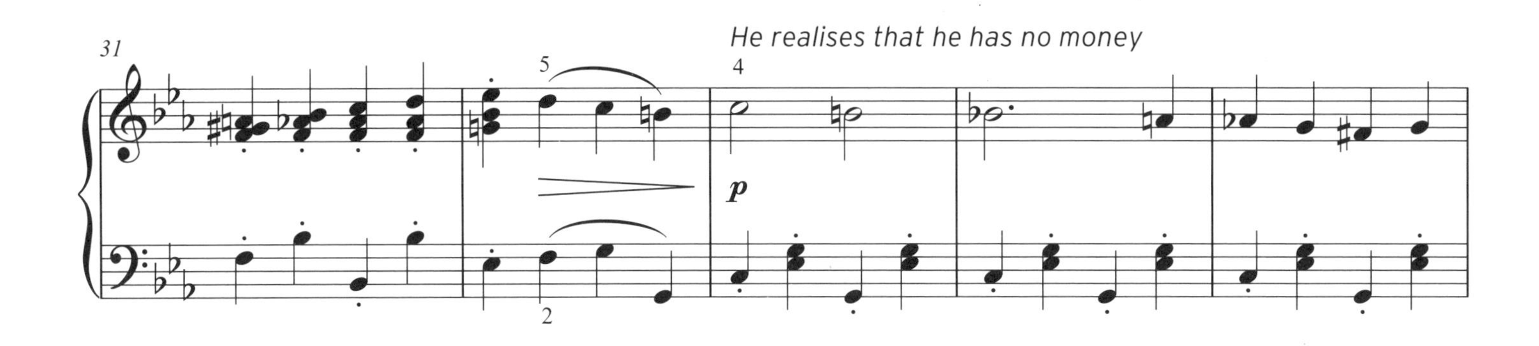
31
He realises that he has no money
p

36
f

41
molto rit.
p

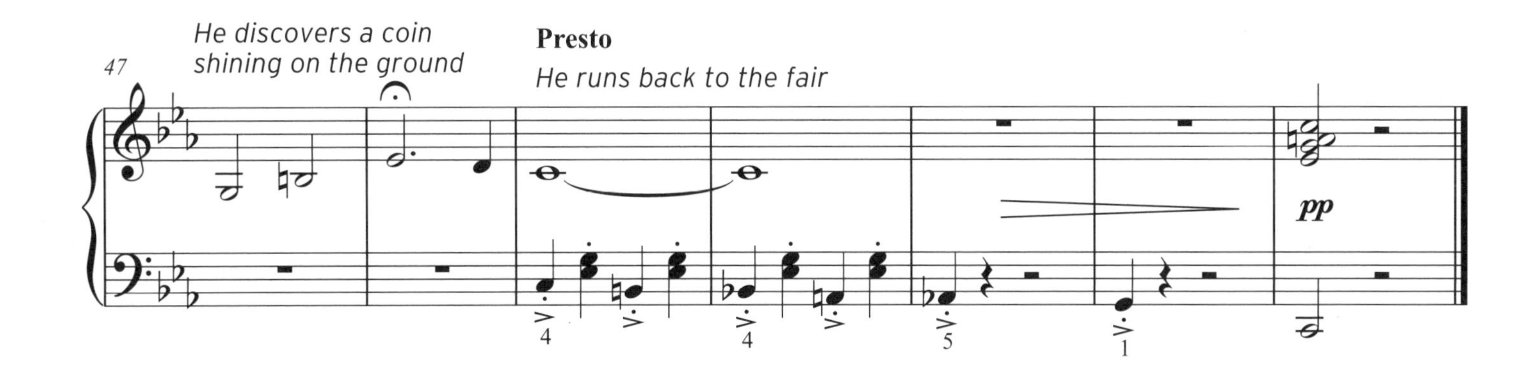
47
He discovers a coin
shining on the ground
Presto
He runs back to the fair
pp

The House Elf's Rag

17
21
25
28
31
p